Mother Penny

by Gertrude Robinson

CONTENTS

INTRODUCTION

THIS IS THE BOOK OF MOTHER PENNY. Mother Penny would rather be wild and hungry than tame and fed.

Mother Penny would rather be free and thirsty than drink water of captivity.

Mother Penny chose to live for a time with men rather than be a bad mother.

This is why we call her Mother Penny. She made us think of a woman named Penelope who chose loyalty to love and duty instead of her own pleasure.

Mother Penny is a Mallard duck. She came from the wild. She went to the wild.

One summer morning she came, she and her ten ducklings. A great storm forced her inland with them.

One fall day she went, because the ten ducklings and one other were strong enough to go with her.

Not until then did she use the strength in her beautiful wings, lined with white like silken clouds, to return to her native island where only wild things lived.

We miss Mother Penny, for we know we are never to see her again. It would be cruel to wish her back. We hope her tameless heart is beating more trustfully because, for a few short months, she lived with us and learned she could be fed and sheltered—and free.

Chapter 1

MOTHER PENNY

THE WIND WENT, "WHIEUH, WHIEUH," higher and higher. Shriller and shriller.

The balsam tree back of the sea wall shivered. It shook off spicy smells. They mixed with salty smells.

The great, wide ocean rushed in. Crash! Crash! Right against the sea wall in front of the little house on the ledges, it made thunder.

One little corner below the sea wall it didn't touch. So far it came, no farther.

1

It never reached that little corner of sand
and pebbles where the wall of stones, set
together, met the wall of ledges.

Salt water, just so far. No farther, ever.
That was why a stout and very tall weed
grew there. Betty called it the horsetail.
It was straight and stiff, a spike, all brown
and seedy.

Something else was there.

Something, just a black blob in moonlight when it slipped between scampering clouds. Something all spread out. Something that made a noise, a soft quacking to answer little piping whistles.

The whistles came from under feathered wings, from under breast feathers. They were fluffed out like an umbrella, all Mother Penny's feathers.

Close to the horsetail stalk she sat, beak to the sea. She loved the feel of salt spray over her head. Mother Penny wasn't afraid of any sea that raced. Not of any wind that blew. She was resting, not because she was tired. Mother Penny could ride the sea and the wind all day and all night. She loved it. Salt spray. Salt water. Winds that tickled her feathers.

Only a strange thing had happened.
Under her feathers were ten baby
ducklings. Little things they were, hardly
yet able to say, "Chee-chee-chee."

They were little whistlers, frail as soap
bubbles.

Now they were lost. Mother Penny
herself was lost.

It had been a bright day with warm sun
when she paddled away from the island
where the ten babies had stepped out of
their shells. They were too tiny to ride the
water far. That didn't matter. She gathered
them under her wings. Some got on her
back.

They slept. They woke up. They let
the gentle water carry them, tiny flat
feet going up, down. Wee paddles, pink

pancakes on green water, were their feet.
They ate bits of green things floating on
the water. They climbed back under warm
feathers to ride.

Babies under a floating pillow, that was
what they were.

They were on the way to a new home.
Mother Penny was wise. She never brought
up her babies where they hatched out
of the nest. She knew about skunks and
weasels and snakes. She was on the way
to a paradise of wild ducks, an island out
at sea. Wild rice grew out there, and there
were grasses gone to seed, and all over
the rocks clung green, salty salads for the
babies to eat. She could stand on her head
in the shallow water near shore and pick up
little shelly things for the babies to whistle

over. When it came cold weather, Mother Penny didn't mind. The babies would be grown. There would be fish washing up on the shore to be eaten. There was a hollow place in the rocks to hide in, out of the wind. There was a spring of fresh water. It went gurgle, gurgle all the time.

Men never came there, not to stay.

Mother Penny was free as the wind. Free as the air.

She knew some ducks went inland to bring up their ducklings instead of out to sea. They had learned to live near those beings with two legs who went on the water in boats. They had learned to stay near the houses where the two-legged beings lived. They had forgotten about bringing up their babies away from the place where the nest had been.

Now it had happened to Mother Penny.

A wind had come along. It had driven a huge wave ahead of it. On the wave was Mother Penny, and beneath her wings were ten bits of fluff on pipe-stem legs mounted on flat pink feet.

The wind carried Mother Penny in from the sea. Right toward the shore of a big island where men lived, it carried her and the wave. Into a long, narrow cove, the wave crowded. It had to rear up like a frightened horse because it couldn't spread out.

Smash it went, against the ledges. Smash it went, against the sea wall in front of the little house.

Then it went back, sweep, surge, bang, against the wind. The wind spanked it in. The something that calls the salt water back to the ocean made it go out.

When the wave went out, it didn't carry Mother Penny with it. Not one of the ten babies. Out the wave went, foaming and spitting, between the rocks that made the mouth of the cove narrow.

Mother Penny wasn't hurt. Not a baby was hurt.

She was just lost.

She knew the sea. She knew the islands out at sea. About this island with houses on it, she knew not one thing.

8

She knew only that she must stay in this bit of a corner where the horsetail stood. Here the ten were safe. They all loved to be on the water, but not under it when big waves were smashed against rocks. One smashing wave and a baby duck would never move again.

Mother Penny knew about all this. She could have gone out, riding that swirling water by herself. She couldn't take the babies—not alive.

Mother Penny was brave. She just sat there with them. She kept them warm and dry.

Mother Penny was wise. When the sea went down and the wind stopped pushing it in, she and the babies would go walking over mud and stone and flats. They'd come to nice green water. They'd ride away on it, out to the sea-washed islands where men never came.

The sun began to make fire out of the place behind the water. Then was when Mother Penny always got sleepy. One little nap and she'd be away.

When she woke up, she couldn't stir. The wind blew as hard as ever, right into the cove. She couldn't move away from the corner beneath the horsetail. Not one of the babies could live in it a second.

The wind kept up. Twice the sun went down. The wind still pinned her under the horsetail. The babies were hungry. The babies were thirsty. "Water," they piped. They made little cracked "Whieus."

Then something happened.

The water of the sea had gone away. Instead, there was water in something black. Fresh water! Good to drink.

The babies were in it, sipping, soaking.

Mother Penny said one sound. It meant, "Come to me!" The babies kept on soaking their pink, webbed feet.

Mother Penny couldn't help it. She didn't step forward, but she stuck out her bill. Closer to the water it came. She took one sip. Another! She was in the pan. Ten ducklings crowded about her.

There was a strange sound.

It was a sound Mother Penny had never heard before. She had heard wind talk and sea talk and bird talk. She had never heard a laugh before.

It came from something that sat on the

steps of the sea wall. There was yellow
fluff on its head, like baby duckling fluff.
Something blue like water came up to the
yellow. The sound came from a red mouth.

Mother Penny was afraid, but not as
afraid as she had been.

The babies were not old enough to be
afraid of anything.

Mother Penny flapped her white-lined
wings once. The wind was going down. She
could fly away. The babies couldn't go with
her. She folded her wings. She called the
babies to her and spread all her feathers
about them. They were safe with her.

The next thing she knew, there was white
stuff in front of her. Not wild rice seeds. It
smelled right, though. The babies ran for
it. They gobbled till their little spoons of

12

bills were full. They raced to the pan to drink. They had soaked up all the water.

Something came down the sea wall steps. Something twice as tall as the thing with yellow fluff on its head. It wore high boots with red flaps that turned down and back again to make cuffs. It talked strange talk. It had red hair and white oilskin clothes.

It poured water into the pan. It knelt. It put down more white stuff, all about. The babies ate. The babies drank.

The tall thing in the red boots bent over.
It kept the wind from whirling the babies
about like thistledown.

Mother Penny gave one crazed quack.
Her bill worked, shot back. She was
hungry. The white stuff smelled right. The
yellow head was down beside the red one.
A big hand was held out, very slowly, right
under Mother Penny's turned-away bill.
A little hand came out, also slowly,
right under Mother Penny's
turned-away bill. In each
was lots of the white,
good-smelling
stuff.

Mother Penny couldn't help it. She took a bill full. She drank water, and she cocked an eye at the sea. It was still too rough. It would smash baby ducklings.

The big thing with the red head made a noise. It meant, "It's time, Betty."

Mother Penny didn't understand what was said. She knew what was done. Red Head put out a hand. It scooped up ten baby ducks. They were so small they were held in it, safe and snug.

Up the steps to the sea wall went the red flap boots.

Down the steps came sounds, whistling "Whieus," almost "Chees."

Mother Penny heard the "Whieus." A mother duck always follows that sound. She'd follow it into fire. Into a hole. Anywhere!

Mother Penny followed. The wind from the sea blew her along. Up the steps she went, waddle, paddle, hop, the wind blowing her tail feathers over her angry head.

Behind her came Yellow Head, the wind blowing her yellow fleece ahead of her.

Straight after the "Whieus" paddled Mother Penny. She stopped. She was under the balsam tree. Before her was a brick pan, abrim with fresh water. About were flat stones, and on them was more of the white stuff. In the pan were ten balls of fluff.

There was only one thing to do. Mother Penny stepped into the pan. She spread her wings. Under them snuggled eight balls of fluff; on her back were two more.

Mother Penny couldn't help it. The time had come for her to be sleepy. The sun was high. Bedtime for ducks! She tucked her head under her wing.

First, though, she sniffed at the ducklings. They smelled right. They were hers. Red Head and Yellow Head hadn't given them the wrong smell for a wild Mallard to sniff.

"Q-U-A-C-K!" Mother Penny was almost asleep.

"W-H-I-E-U!" piped the ten babies.

Yellow Head made a sound. What it meant was, "She'll stay."

Red Head made a sound. What it meant was, "She'd fly this minute—if the little whistlers could."

Chapter 2

THE LITTLEST WHISTLER

THE LITTLEST WHISTLER SAT ALONE. The flat stone was warm. The blue water was just an inch high about it. His little pink flat feet made sucking noises in it. He lifted them up, down, up, down.

"Quack! Quackety! Quack!" That was Mother Brown Mallard paddling away.

"Chee-chee-chee-chee," soft, like water lapping. That was his eight brothers and sisters.

Littlest Whistler didn't want to hear. Not at first. Then he had a strange, new feeling. He was warm, but he was lonesome. He began to make soft little breaths of sound. He couldn't go, "Chee-chee-chee," like the others. He couldn't do anything but whistle.

Mother Brown Duck didn't hear. She kept swimming farther away. After 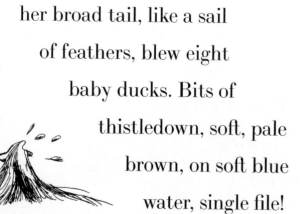 her broad tail, like a sail of feathers, blew eight baby ducks. Bits of thistledown, soft, pale brown, on soft blue water, single file!

Just a string of blown feathers!

Littlest Whistler wanted to be on the end of that string. He jumped off the flat, warm rock. There wasn't any water anymore. Just mud. Warm, sticky mud! His feet stuck fast in it.

Littlest Whistler had streaky brown down on his bit of a body. The wind blew it every which way. It blew the down away from his back like foam on milk.

He was all shivers. He couldn't even pipe a breath of a whistle. The blue water was going farther and farther away. Out with it sailed Mother Brown Duck. Out with it blew along the eight. They were all bigger than the Littlest Whistler. They had found out how to go "Chee-chee-chee." He could hear them. He tried to go "Chee-chee-chee."

His little throat was too dry to let out even one whistle.

Then he heard something else. Something that came plop, plop, plop over the mud.

Littlest Whistler froze. Already Mother Brown Duck had taught him that before he was two hours out of the shell. He made himself look like a flat chunk of brown mud, all so still.

The plopping came nearer. It stopped beside him. Something took him right up, out of the mud, all so gently. Something

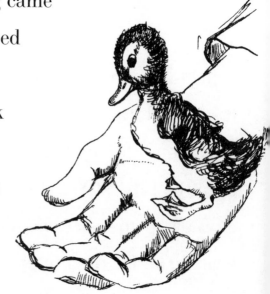

warm and gentle, only with no soft feathers to snuggle in.

There were strange sounds, right in his ear. He didn't know what they meant. He was so frightened he opened his tiny beak and a wee whistle came out. "Whi-eu! Whi-eu," he said.

What the sounds really meant was, "Look, Betty, a lost baby duck. His mother will never know she's lost him. Mother ducks can't count. They can only listen." That was a loud sound, like water on rocks.

The other sound was smaller, like the tide coming in through the water reeds. What it meant was, "We'll take him home and give him to our wild Mother Penny when she brings home her ten babies in the morning to get breakfast in the yard."

Littlest Whistler wasn't afraid anymore. There he was in a soft cave made of Betty's old wool sweater. There was a tiny saucer with oat flakes in it before him and a tiny dish with fresh water in it. The first thing he did when Betty's fingers put him down was to get into the dish of water. He sipped and sat, sat and sipped. He drank and ate, ate and drank.

When his flat feet were all soaked and cool, he crept back into the woolly cave. It felt like his mother's breast, speckled and feathery, all about him.

There were sounds going on.

"Early in the morning," said Betty, "Mother Penny will bring her ten wild babies up the steps to the sea wall. They will all go to the drinking pan. I'll put Littlest Whistler down with them."

"She mustn't ever know," said Jimmy. "If he makes one bit of a 'Whieu' before he's with the others, she'll never own him."

The sounds went on. Littlest Whistler didn't mind. He just knew there was water. There was food. There was something warm to snuggle into.

Betty went to bed. The clock struck eight.

The clock struck five. Betty woke up.

She slipped into her blue bathrobe. She ran out to the porch. Littlest Whistler was all warm and sleepy. She picked him up in her fingers. He was warm and soft as a ripe dandelion.

Out on the blue-as-sky cove a big duck was riding, tail spread like a sail on the incoming tide. The sun was up. It had popped out of the water a long time before.

The water was gold and blue and morning-glad.

Out of the water and into the sandy cove and up the sea wall steps came wild Mother Penny. Ten wisps of down paddled like mad after her. They were all talking, saying, "Chee-chee-chee."

Littlest Whistler, deep in Betty's warm pocket, heard them. He gave one little "Whieu." Betty held his flat beak closed to keep him from giving another too soon.

No wonder he heard them. Right up the steps came wild Mother Penny's brownish pink feet, like pancakes. Right up the steps came little pink feet, pit-pat. Not all of them. Some babies just hopped and hopped and fell back. They were all going, "Chee-chee-chee," wildly.

Jimmy, all tousle-headed, came to see what was happening.

Red Head in tall red-flapped boots came up the cove in his boat to see what was happening.

Mother Penny was up the steps. She stood at the top and quacked and quacked to call the timid babies after her. Uncle Peter Drake and Uncle Piper Drake swam about in the cove. Not too near. They knew better than to come near. Only Mother Penny had anything to do with baby ducks. Their green necklaces shone in the sun. Betty hoped Littlest Whistler would grow up to have a green neckband and burnished blue bars on his wings.

Up the last step hopped one of the slow ducklings. Another came. Another. Mother Penny kept turning her head and looking at Betty instead of at the ducklings. Did she hear the little breath of whistle coming from Betty's pocket?

Five were up the steps. Six were up. Seven and eight and nine and ten couldn't make it. Mother Penny waddled to the edge of the wall. She looked over. She quacked, scolding quacks.

"Now," whispered Jimmy.

"Now," beckoned Red Head from his boat.

Betty was racing down the yard. She dropped Littlest Whistler right down in the midst of the six brave ducklings.

The six babies were not waiting for Mother Penny and the other four. They were eating oat flakes. They were in the brick pan together.

Mother Penny came waddling. At her tail were all the slow babies. In no time at all, Mother Penny was in the pan of fresh water herself, just as though she hadn't been in a whole salt ocean most of the night.

She was in the pan of water with ten

little ducklings going "Chee-chee-chee." She was in the pan with one little duckling going "Whieu-whieu-whieu."

Then it happened. Mother Penny flapped her beautiful brown wings lined with white as soft as a fleecy cloud. She flipped water everywhere. Her wings came down. Under them was every duckling but one.

On her back rode one little duckling, a wee duckling. He opened his bit of a flat bill, and he said, "Whieu! Whieu! Whieu!"

Mother Penny tucked her head under her wing. Ten baby ducks under her feathers tucked in their heads under tiny wings.

One baby duck on Mother Penny's back tucked his head into her soft neck feathers. Mother Penny's breast rose, fell. They were all having their first nap of the day.

"She's owned him," said Red Head.

"She's owned him," said Yellow Head.

Littlest Whistler stirred. It was like the wind moving the sprills of the little balsam tree; all these sounds he didn't fear.

Chapter 3

THE LOBSTER CAR

IT WAS A SHINING MORNING. Betty put on her blue bathing suit and her red sandals when she got out of bed. Over her bathing suit, she had her fleecy Turkish toweling cape, red inside, blue outside.

"Hurry," cried Jimmy. "Where's old Mother Penny and Littlest Whistler?"

Betty ran. Mother ran.

No brown and black Penny with freckles on her breast.

No ten ducklings like fat brown thistleheads on pink legs.

No Littlest Whistler, all fluffy still and downy. He had just learned to go, "Chee-chee-chee," like the others, instead of saying one little "Whieu" after another.

There was breakfast in little heaps on the flat stones, a big stone for Mother Penny because Littlest Whistler always stood on it to eat with her.

There was the brick pan, running over with water.

Betty's breath came in little gasps when she saw the water in the pan was clean. No little ducks were in it. No little ducks had been

in it. It ought to be spilling over with little ducks, swimming, soaking, drinking all at once.

Betty closed her eyes. That way she could just see them, the way they ought to be. Each would take a beakful. Each would lift a head. That was because they said thanks before they swallowed.

"Listen," cried Jimmy. He stood on the top of the sea wall, all black bathing suit and brown arms and legs. He pointed toward the other side of the cove.

"Baby ducks! Afraid! Mother Penny calling to them," cried Betty. She began to run.

It was true. Across the mud flats came hundreds of "Chee-chee-chees." Across the place where the blue water had run, one was more shrill than all the others. Part "Chee-chee-chee," it went, part "Whieu-whieu-whieu."

"Littlest Whistler," said Betty, and ran faster, her feet sucking through the soft mud of the flats.

"Littlest Whistler," shouted Jimmy, far ahead.

There it was, the big lobster car. That was what the lobstermen called it. It was a great box, like a room with a flat top. There were slats across the top. In the car the lobstermen put the lobsters they took out of the cages in the cove. Twice a day the tide came in and filled the car. Twice a day the tide slowly leaked out.

Jimmy was on top of the car. He was looking between the slats.

"No lobsters inside," he shouted. "Just all Mother Penny's babies."

Betty climbed to the top of the car. She looked between the slats. There they were: eleven little ducks. They were cheeing and racing about like crazy brown crickets.

Outside the cage was Mother Penny. She ran around and around it, trying to get inside. She flew to the top of the car and tried to squeeze between the slats. She was too big.

All the time she was saying so many quacks even Betty couldn't tell where one left off and the other began.

For once Jimmy wasn't laughing. "Mother Penny'll go crazy," he said. "They'll have to stay inside and she outside until the tide comes back and they can swim up on it. Up and up it will lift them until they can swim out through the places between the slats at the top."

"That's how they got in," said Betty. "They've been in here for hours and hours."

"They'll be in the car hours and hours more." Jimmy slipped down from the top of the car. "We might as well go home and get oat flakes to throw down to them. Mother Penny'll split her throat quacking to them."

"No, she won't," answered Betty. She slipped down from the top of the car. She ran out across the mud flats to the rocks that turned the inner cove almost into a pond except at low water and high water. She took off her fleecy coat and waved it.

Three men in the motorboat chugging

out to look at lobster cages in the deep
water saw her. They turned the boat and
came racing in.

"What's the matter, Betty?" asked one.
He jumped out of the boat, because the
water was too shallow to float it, and
climbed up the rock.

"Eleven baby ducks. Your lobster car.
Mother Penny's going mad," gasped Betty.

"My word!" The lobsterman called
to the two men in the boat. "It's baby
ducks we've been hearing all morning."
He tramped down the rocks in his big hip
boots, with high red flaps turned down
at the top to make a cuff. He was all
red-flapped high boots and white oilskin
clothes and bare red head.

Betty ran beside him, hand in his. Over

brown warm mud, over patches of white sand they raced right up to the lobster car.

Mother Penny didn't understand about the lobsterman. She pecked at his rubber boots. Her broad bill slid off them with funny noises, like a spoon slipping down the side of a bowl of oatmeal. She was all swollen up, and her tail was spread, and her wings beat at the lobsterman's legs.

"She thinks I did it," he said. He got on top the car. Betty swarmed after him, stepping on uneven places in the boards.

By the time she was up, the lobsterman had lifted four slats where there was a hinge to get lobsters in and out. He and Jimmy were down inside with eleven ducklings and a great deal of seaweed.

"Stay where you are," he said to Betty.

"We'll hand them up to you."

He and Jimmy were down on their knees in wet seaweed. One by one they caught baby ducks and passed them up to Betty. Mother Penny danced below on flat pancake feet until the first duckling got away from between Betty's fingers. Over the edge of the car it went, blown thistledown. It landed on flat pink feet.

Mother Penny stopped hopping up and down like a heap of mad feathers. She stopped in the middle of a quack. She started for home, the one duckling paddling after her.

Betty knew then it was true. Mother Penny was bad in numbers. One duckling or eleven made her just as happy. That is, unless she could hear the ones left behind.

Up they came, two, three, four, five, six, seven, eight, nine, ten.

No more.

The lobsterman's red head came up through the opening.

"How many'd you say there are?"

"Eleven." Betty was near crying again. "The dearest one of them all, Littlest Whistler, is down there."

The lobsterman looked after the mites skidding for home behind Mother Penny. He counted. "Ten," he said. "Doesn't she know there's one more?"

"She can't count," explained Betty. "It's all right with her if she doesn't hear one somewhere else. I don't hear him either. Yes, I *do*, down there with you and Jimmy."

Across the mud flats, into the home cove went a broad-tailed, waddling brown duck. After Mother Penny went ten bits of things on pink feet, funny quills starting out of their down. They made such a chee-cheeing, it was no wonder Mother Penny didn't hear Littlest Whistler whistling and cheeing away, all by himself.

"He's down there," said Betty.

"He's down there," said Jimmy. "But where?"

"He's here," said the red-headed lobsterman. "I hear him. But where?"

He went back down on his hands and knees and picked up wads of seaweed. Jimmy went down on hands and knees and picked up wads of seaweed. Betty knelt at the edge of the place where the slats were lifted and looked and looked.

Everywhere they went. The lobsterman's face got as red as his hair. It got as red as the turned-down-and-over cuffs of his hip-length boots. He and Jimmy lifted every mite of seaweed and dug fingers into every hole.

"He's right near," said the lobsterman. "He can't be hurt. He's making lots of noise."

He dug a little hole in the mud and sand where the lobster car sat on the floor of the cove. It was big enough for Littlest Whistler to go through and too small for a lobster.

"Don't you worry, Betty," said Red Head. "When he gets over being frightened, he'll find his way out and run for home. He's hiding somewhere. But where?"

He climbed out.

Jimmy climbed out.

They put back the slats.

Jimmy jumped down.

Betty jumped down.

The lobsterman jumped down.

Something else jumped.

Something so small eleven of him could have sat on the palm of the lobsterman's big, kind hand. Something all fluff. Something that whistled in the middle of a "Chee-chee-chee!"

"The little duffer!" said the lobsterman.

Jimmy said nothing. His mouth hung open.

Betty said nothing. She was too busy turning crying into laughing.

They had all seen where Littlest Whistler jumped from.

He jumped out of the half-turned-down, half-turned-up red flap of the lobsterman's boots.

There he was, making for home on flat pink feet over warm mud. He whistled as he went.

When Betty and Jimmy got home, there was Littlest Whistler. His little spoon of a bill showed flecks of oat flake porridge. He was sitting on Mother Penny's back, sound asleep in the sun.

Chapter 4

THE FISH NET

M OTHER PENNY WAS IN TROUBLE.
Littlest Whistler heard her.

"Q-U-A-C-K! Q-U-A-C-K!—Q-U-A-Q-U-A—"

Littlest Whistler tried to run. He tried
to fly. He stepped on his own two big feet.

He just didn't
get anywhere.

Once he
blew along like
thistledown.

Now he was getting real wings and a tail that turned up in a stiff point. He was covered with little sharp, prickly quills. They all got in his way. The tail made him spin this way, that way in the wind, like a silly top. The wings went up, down. They were no good at all.

The quills were the worst, though. They stuck out all over him like stout pins. They were not down. They were not feathers.

Littlest Whistler looked as though he had been rolled over and over in a bed of dead flower stalks. They felt that way, too.

How he missed Mother Penny! She had been away ever since the sun came out of the water like a red pumpkin. He had seen her when she went away. Her feet padded right down the green lane toward the ledges. He had started after her. All his ten brothers and sisters started after her.

Mother Penny had turned, once. She made one funny quack.

They all went home to sit under the balsam tree. They knew what that quack meant. It was, "Stay where you are till I come back."

Littlest Whistler minded. All of them minded. Baby ducklings nearly always mind. That is the way their mothers teach them.

Mother Penny was teaching them to take naps by themselves. Littlest Whistler understood. They all snuggled up to him. He had outgrown all of them. Once he was the tiniest. Now he was the biggest. They could almost get under his wings. He felt important. Then he took a nap.

It was when he woke up that he heard Mother Penny.

"Q-U-A-C-K! Q-U-A-C-K!—Q-U-A-Q-U-A—," she said.

She was calling to him, her biggest duckling. She was proud of him. She knew that in no time, he'd be a smart young drake with a green neck and a loud voice.

That was when he started running,
flying, scrambling on his flat feet that were
so big he stepped on them. One foot over,
one foot under. One foot under, one foot
over—he got them to going right.

They took him to the place where
Mother Penny sat in the hollow in the
rocks.

Over her was something. Something all
brown and wet and smelling of fish.

Littlest Whistler didn't know how it got
there. Mother Penny didn't either. She had
been sound asleep, just for a minute, when
the fishermen had dragged the net out of
the boat and spread it out on the rocks
to dry. They spread it right over Mother
Penny. She was all brown and gray and
black like the rocks.

Now she was awake. Littlest Whistler saw her try to spread her wings. The net caught at them. He saw her try to stand up. The net twisted about her big, flat feet. She lifted her head, and the net let her beak go right through.

All of Mother Penny that was free, free as air, was just the tip of her spoon of a bill.

She could open her bill, and she said one more frightened, "Quack!"

That was when Littlest Whistler rolled and flew and paddled right over the big spreading net. He got to Mother Penny. He said, "CHEE-CHEE-CHEE-WHEE-WHEE-WHIEU!"

He tried to get through the meshes of the net, in beside Mother Penny.

He was too big.

The more he tried, the more his feet were caught in the holes of the net. He whistled. Mother Penny quacked. All the other baby ducklings heard. They came, bits of flying windblown things.

Through the lane. Over the net. There they stopped. Even they were too large to squirm through the holes in it. All their feet were caught in the net. All their bits of half wings were fast in it.

Mother Penny nearly quacked herself hoarse, telling them to go away. Littlest Whistler made whistles and chees, all at once. The other ducklings made sounds like little frightened, crying winds.

Betty, taking her dip in the shining pool the high tide left on the shore, heard the noise.

The red-headed fisherman heard it.
Betty came running, her bathing cape over
her shoulders. The fisherman came, taking
long strides. His long boots with red flaps
turned down, then up, quashed over the
rocks.

Betty and the fisherman got to the net
together. He took the floppy hat off his red

head. Betty caught one little quiller after another. They weren't really ducklings anymore. They were covered with quills, between down and feathers. They were homely little things, homely little quillers. Mother Penny loved them more than ever. She made a terrible fuss when she saw Betty putting them in the fisherman's hat. She made more fuss when Betty tucked her cape over them so they couldn't hop out.

Then they began on Mother Penny. Betty knew the net mustn't be cut. Nets cost money, a great deal. With a torn net, the fisherman couldn't keep the fish that got into it.

Mother Penny was so scared now she didn't make a sound. She was all limp and cold while Betty helped the fisherman get

the ends of her feathers out of the holes
in the net. As fast as they got one feather
loose, another was caught.

"Go down to the lower edge of the net
and crawl under," said the fisherman to
Betty.

Betty looked at the net. It was fishy, and
it smelled.

"Plucky girl," said the fisherman, just as
though she meant to do it.

Down the ledges to where the net began
ran Betty. She got down on the rocks, and
she crawled in under the smelly net. She
went crawling up under the net, slowly, not
to set Mother Penny squirming again. She
reached Mother Penny.

She put her hands over Mother Penny's
back. She smoothed all the ends of the

feathers free, and she held Mother Penny still so she couldn't get all tangled up again.

Mother Penny was soft. Her feathers were like silk. She ought to feel like a warm, feathery ball. She didn't. She was so frightened she was limp and cold.

"Talk to her," said the fisherman.

Betty talked. She held Mother Penny's brownish-pink feet in her hands. She tucked Mother Penny's bill under her arm.

Mother Penny was safe, but she didn't know it. Her bill went open, shut. Betty was afraid Mother Penny would die.

"Hurry," said Betty.

The red-headed fisherman was lifting the heavy net in front of Betty. Two more fishermen came, clomp, clomp, in big boots. They pulled up the net, a few feet at a time. Betty crawled on toward the upper edge where the net ran into green grass.

Mother Penny was still limp. The net caught in Betty's hair. The fishermen kept going, a foot at a time, a foot at a time— Would they never lift the last foot?

One more tug.

The net was off her.

The net was off Mother Penny.

Mother Penny wasn't dead. She gave one long, breathless sigh of a quack.

Then she was out of Betty's arms. Paddle, paddle, waddle, waddle she went. Along the green lane she went. Toward the balsam tree! Toward the brick pan! Toward home!

The fishermen stood in the lane and

watched. Red Head stooped. He tipped up
his hat on the ground. Out popped Littlest
Whistler.

Out popped one, two, three—ten little
quillers. Littlest Whistler was ahead. He
ran after Mother Penny. The ten chased
after him.

Mother Penny was in the pan of water,
cleaning her feathers. Ten little quillers
were in with her. Littlest Whistler jumped
to her back.

Just as usual.

It was once too often.

Mother Penny shook herself. Water flew all about. Littlest Whistler went off. He landed on his feet, outside the pan.

He opened his bill and said something. It sounded almost like a quack.

Betty dropped down on the grass. The red-headed fisherman dropped down on the grass. They saw Mother Penny swell and swell. Her feathers were clean. They stood out like a great pillow. Mother Penny was proud. They saw her spread her wings.

Ten quillers snuggled under them. They were so big they stuck out, all around.

Only Littlest Whistler didn't get under the wings. He was grown up. That was why Mother Penny was proud. He squatted down beside her.

Mother Penny tucked her head under
her wing. Littlest Whistler tucked his head
under his wing. He and Mother Penny
were having a grownup nap together.

Chapter 5

MOTHER PENNY IS LOST

LITTLEST WHISTLER OPENED ONE BLACK eye. He opened the other very fast.

There was Mother Penny waddling, all alone, down the steps of the sea wall.

Then she spoke. It was her "Come with me" quack.

Right away ten little awkward quillers were hopping, racing, trying to fly—all in a hurry to get to her. They stepped on their own feet.

Right through the petunia bed they

went. Out to the sea wall. They fell down. They half flew down. They didn't wait for the steps.

Littlest Whistler was sleepy. He stretched one leg. Another leg. He felt very large and strong. His feathers were grown now, not just quills. He was getting black and brown, not just brownish and

yellowish and blackish anymore. He had
a big voice. He could talk back to Uncle
Peter and to Uncle Piper down in the
water.

Sometimes he started to go down and
swim about with them. Mother Penny
always stopped him. She had a funny kind
of a quack that meant, "No, stay by me,
silly thing."

Now was his chance. Mother Penny
was waddling off, fast as she could go. She
was in the water. She was sailing right out
into the wind. After her went big blackish
specks on the water, ten of them. She
couldn't count. She'd never know he wasn't
along if he didn't make a noise she could
hear.

He went through the petunia bed.

He flipped his upstanding tail at Susie, the cat, on the steps. He pretended to be afraid of the little curly dog, Raffles. Raffles liked to run along the sea wall, nipping off nasturtium buds with his sharp teeth. He liked to bark at Littlest Whistler.

Littlest Whistler liked to tease Raffles. Now he didn't stop. He hopped, flew, and tumbled down the sea wall steps. He no longer hopped down each one. He couldn't really fly. Still, his wings were getting strong and firm. He no longer stepped on his own feet.

He lifted his head to call to Uncle Peter, who had been down in the cove a minute ago. Uncle Peter was gone. Uncle Piper was gone. Not a duck in sight except

Mother Penny, paddling away as fast as she could.

Yes, there was something on the water. Right near. Blue bars on its wings, green on its neck. Something big and broad—it was a strange new drake.

Littlest Whistler didn't like him. He knew why Mother Penny went away with her family, fast as she could go. He knew why Uncle Peter and Uncle Piper had gone away. He knew why there wasn't a duck,

big or little, except him, Littlest Whistler, anywhere about.

Littlest Whistler felt big and important. He threw out his neck so it was long for him. He said a small quack at the strange pirate of a drake.

It meant, "Stay away from here!"

The strange drake didn't answer. At once he came swimming right into the cove past the rocks. His eyes were beady.

He wasn't a kind old drake, like Uncle Peter and Uncle Piper. Littlest Whistler forgot to be big and important. He ran–hopped–tumbled. In no time at all, he was in the water. He was going like mad after Mother Penny.

There was where he belonged, right beside her. The others swam all about.

They were getting so big and bold they no longer went in a tight wedge back of her tail. They were growing up, only not so fast as Littlest Whistler.

He caught up with Mother Penny. He cocked his head back. Pirate drake was coming after them, not very fast. He was coming, though. He looked like a mountain on the water, a black, cross mountain. His eyes were red-black. Littlest Whistler snuggled close to Mother Penny.

She did a strange thing. She nipped him, hard, with her beak. She made a sound. It meant, "Swim behind the others. Keep them close behind me."

Littlest Whistler got behind the others. He nipped the ones that tried to go by themselves. He understood. Mother Penny

was afraid of the new, strange drake. She was getting them all out of sight, as fast as she could.

Mother Penny paddled fast. The ten quillers paddled fast. Littlest Whistler paddled fast.

Once again he looked back. He couldn't see the strange drake with fire in his eyes. Mother Penny had guided them around a big rocky point. That was why.

On she went, a long way.

Down the cove, past the fish houses.

They never stopped to peck at bits of fish. Out of the little cove and into the big cove that rubbed shoulders with the ocean. The air was salt, and the water was salt, and Littlest Whistler forgot to be afraid.

Mother Penny hadn't though. She kept in close along the shore of the little island where the red-headed fisherman lived. She swept past it, past another little island, and then she vanished!

Littlest Whistler was afraid now. He just kept going after the ten.

They vanished.

Another minute and he was in a strange place. He had gone right into a hole in the rocky shore. The hole went on and on. There was water in it. Then, ahead, he saw Mother Penny. She was half swimming, half walking. The ten quillers were close behind her. He paddled fast and walked fast. He caught up with them. He felt safe again.

They went on and on in the half dark. Then it was light. Mother Penny had led them all straight to another hole in the rocks. They went through it into sunlight.

Littlest Whistler had never seen the new cove before. There they were, ten little quillers, Mother Penny, and him. They were swimming in a wide, shallow cove.

There was white sand underneath. He
could see bits of crabs and snails and salty
green things in the sand.

Mother Penny wasn't afraid anymore.
She was standing on her head in the water,
nipping up green, salty things. He stood
on his head, the way she did. He was big
enough for that. When he got back, head
up, he could see the ten quillers racing
along the shore. They were picking up food.

Food! Food! Food! Food everywhere.
There was water, fresh water, coming
out of something long and black in the
rocks at the back of the cove. The water
splashed and spattered. It sounded
cool. Mother Penny went up and got
a drink. The ten quillers raced up and
drank. Littlest Whistler stopped eating a
sunburned crab and went for a drink.

He drank and guzzled and washed in the
splashing water. He took a long time.

When he'd had enough and turned
around to go back to the cove, he was
alone.

No Mother Penny! No ten quillers like black specks!

He was alone. Nothing moved except a boat a long way off, moving away from the shore.

Littlest Whistler couldn't even make a half quack.

He got in the water, and he didn't know which way to go. Then he saw the hole in the rock.

That was the way home. He went in. He swam through the tunnel. He came out the other side. Way ahead was the home cove.

He forgot about the strange drake who had been in the water in the home cove. He went home as fast as he could. After a long, long time, he was going up the steps of the sea wall. He was under the balsam tree.

There was the brick pan, full of shining water. There were the oatmeal flakes on flat stones. There was—

No, it wasn't Mother Penny.

It was just the little curly dog, Raffles, asleep, curled up in the sun, black curls, brownish in the sun. It was just Yellow Head beside him. It was just Susie cat on the steps.

"Littlest Whistler," cried Betty, "where's Mother Penny?" Littlest Whistler didn't know words. He did know meanings. He knew Mother Penny was lost.

He went right back down the sea wall. He started paddling away. He found the hole in the rocks. He went through the tunnel. He came out on the shining cove.

Everything was still except for that same boat, moving out to sea.

Littlest Whistler listened. Across the quiet water came a sound he knew. Mother Penny was on that boat. She was crying to him!

Littlest Whistler forgot to be afraid. He began to paddle after the boat as fast as his pink feet could come up, go down, come up, go down.

As he got nearer the boat, he heard other sounds, little half chee-chee-chees, half whistles. He knew that on the boat was Mother Penny, and with her were the ten quillers. Soon he could see them. He could see a pen on the boat. From it came sounds. Mother Penny was in that pen. The quillers were coming in and out through the bars of the pen.

Somebody was stealing Mother Penny. He smelled fresh water on the boat. He

smelled corn flung about. Food and drink
for Mother Penny! Mother Penny who was
wild as the wind, free as the air!

Mother Penny had seen him. She made
one sound. It meant, "Stay where you
are." She made another sound to the
ten quillers. It meant, "Go to Littlest
Whistler."

They came. They tumbled over the edge
of the boat between the bars of the railing.
One, two, three—ten.

"Go away. Take them home." That
was what Mother Penny meant in
the sounds she was making.
Littlest Whistler
started back

toward the hole in the rocks. He looked
over his shoulder. They were coming, all
ten. They made a wedge back of his tail.

He looked back a second time. The boat
was moving fast, out to sea. He could
make out the pen. Mother Penny was still.

They were in the home cove. He went
past the strange new drake. Some of his
feathers were pulled out. He didn't look
fierce. Uncle Peter and Uncle Piper had
been seeing to him. He went by Uncle

Peter and Uncle Piper. He didn't say anything. They didn't even look at him.

Could it be they were ashamed of a young drake being nurse to ten little quillers?

"Where's Mother Penny?" asked Betty as he led the way up the sea wall steps.

"Where's Mother Penny?" called the red-headed fisherman from his boat.

Littlest Whistler had no way to make them understand. He knew what had happened to Mother Penny. Somebody had stolen her. Somebody was taking her away. He knew Mother Penny would get away. She had to. She was wild as the wind, free as the air!

He just got in the pan of water to soak his feet. The ten got in with him. They all went to sleep. They were fed. They were clean. Littlest Whistler! Mother Penny! They hardly knew the difference.

Only Littlest Whistler missed Mother Penny.

Chapter 6

MOTHER PENNY COMES HOME

BETTY SAT ON THE SEA WALL STEPS AND watched for Mother Penny.

The red-headed fisherman watched from his motorboat. He laid nets and kept an eye on ducks.

Littlest Whistler didn't watch. He knew better. He knew what had happened to Mother Penny.

Mother Penny was shut up in a pen. She was on her way out to sea. He had to play Mother Penny to ten little quillers.

Then something happened. Something came down the lane. It was long and high, and it walked right along because men's legs were under it.

The legs bent. They put the long thing down, took off the cover.

Betty came running. The red-headed fisherman came running. Jimmy came running. They all talked at once.

Before Littlest Whistler could make one halfway quack, he had been picked up. He was in the long thing. It was so deep he couldn't jump out. He could see, though. There were little round holes in the sides.

The men were on their knees. They were picking little quillers out of the petunia bed. Out of the brick pan. One, two, three—all ten little quillers were put in with him. The cover of the long thing was put on.

The long thing began to move. Littlest Whistler and the ten quillers tumbled about. The men talked. What the red-headed fisherman said was, "This banana crate is as big as a barn for those ducklings."

Littlest Whistler didn't understand what was said. He wasn't afraid anymore, though. He liked the sound of the red-headed fisherman's voice.

The crate didn't walk very far. It was set down, gently. There was a big noise. After it stopped, Littlest Whistler found a hole in the side of the crate. He went through it. There was a pan of fresh water. There was a pan of salt water. There were oat flakes and corn spread about.

He tried to walk away, right down to the water. He couldn't. There was a lot of wire netting that shut him in. It shut all the ten quillers in. They could never get out. Nothing could ever get in unless somebody opened the gate.

Not a skunk. Not a weasel. Not a rat. Not a bad cat. Not a strange dog. They could go under a cover and keep their feathers dry. They could come out and get in the pan of water and get their feet wet. They could eat, fast as lightning. Salt water! Fresh water! Lots to eat! Safe, everything that could hurt them shut out!

What more could ten little quillers want? What more could Littlest Whistler want?

He could have told them if he had known how.

They wanted Mother Penny.

They wanted to be free, free as air, free as the wind.

The sun went down. The sun came up. It did it again.

Littlest Whistler raced about the net that shut in the yard. He wanted to go swimming out on the big salt water. He tried to tear a hole in the net. His bill was like putty on the net. He could see salt water, lots of it. He could smell it. He could hear Uncle Peter and Uncle Piper, swimming about at night, free as the wind.

He was shut in, he, Littlest Whistler.

He couldn't eat. He could just drink. He could always drink.

Betty came to see them. After her padded Raffles. After him purred Susie, the cat. They all looked sorry for Littlest Whistler and ten little quillers.

Littlest Whistler opened his bill and almost made a quack.

"Let me out! Let me out!" he meant.

Betty understood, but she shook her yellow head. She went away. Raffles went away. Susie went away. They were all sad. They missed Mother Penny.

It was almost sunset again.

Uncle Peter was talking from the cove. Loud and excited. Uncle Piper talked from the cove. Loud and excited.

85

Littlest Whistler went close to the wire netting and looked. He jumped up and down. He was all springs. He almost made a quack.

Coming up the steps of the sea wall was—MOTHER PENNY.

She was little looking, all her feathers

matted down. She was dirty. She was so tired she could hardly stand.

She was—MOTHER PENNY.

Littlest Whistler began to talk louder. The ten quillers began to shriek, one shrill "Chee-chee-chee!" after another. Mother Penny found her voice. She made one excited quack after another. They spilled out of her beak like popping corn sounds.

Betty came running. Red Head came up from his boat, all in a hurry. Yellow Susie came, looking as though she had known it all along. Curly Raffles sat down in the path and exploded into barks.

Mother Penny waddled straight to the wire fence. She stopped before it. Littlest Whistler stuck his bill out through the meshes of the wire. Mother Penny stuck her bill in. All the ten quillers stuck their bills out.

Betty opened the gate to the yard. Mother Penny marched through.

Home! No. Not for Mother Penny. Not yet.

She got in the pan and soaked her feet. She ate corn. She sniffed at each one of the ten quillers. All hers. She rubbed bills with Littlest Whistler.

Then she waddled straight to the wire net. She made one loud quack.

The red-headed fisherman knew what she wanted. Betty knew.

The red-headed fisherman took clippers. He cut here. He cut there. The wire net was down.

Out came Mother Penny. Out came

Littlest Whistler. Out came ten little quillers.

Mother Penny led the way. Straight to the mossy bed under the little balsam tree she went. She settled down. Under her wings snuggled ten little quillers. Close behind her squatted Littlest Whistler.

What did he care about skunks? About rats? About weasels?

He and Mother Penny would guard the ten little quillers.

He and Mother Penny would take them down the steps to swim in the light of the moon. He and Mother Penny would bring them back for another nap.

Up the steps. Down again. Up, down!

Free as the air. Wild as the wind. Safe and free.

Only tonight Mother Penny didn't go swimming. Littlest Whistler knew why. She was tired. She had watched her chance. She had gotten out of that pen, wherever it had been put. She had made for the water. She had come swimming home, straight as a string. Miles and miles of blue water she had crossed. She had come to keep Littlest Whistler and ten little quillers free.

Littlest Whistler stirred and almost quacked. Someday, when the ten little quillers were as big as he was, they would be able to swim far and long. Then Mother Penny would lead them away from the safe cove. Away from the island where men lived. Away from the oat flakes and the strewn corn and the pan of water.

Out to sea she would lead them.

Out to the island she knew, where wild rice ripened for wild ducks to eat. Where salty things were to be nipped from sandbars. Where no men came to catch Mother Penny or the ten quillers or him, Littlest Whistler. Where there was no pen for them and no wire net to shut them in.

They'd be free as air. Wild as the wind.

Wild ducks forever.

THE END